Word Pe
Spelling

BOOK FOUR

BY

RONALD RIDOUT

ILLUSTRATED BY
GEORGE W. ADAMSON, M.S.I.A.

Ginn and Company Ltd

BOOKS BY THE SAME AUTHOR

Write in English, Introductory Books 1 and 2 and Books 1-8: a new style of English Workbook providing a carefully graded course on understanding, using and writing English for all 6- to 12-year olds.

Better English, Introductory Book and Books 1-5: a complete English course from about 6-12 years; illustrated in colour.

English Workbooks, Introductory Books 1 and 2 and Books 1-8: a graded course in punctuation, spelling, vocabulary, comprehension and composition. The first two are intended for infants.

English Workbooks for the Caribbean, Books 1-8: a workbook course specially written for primary schools in the Caribbean; also suitable for immigrants; illustrated in colour.

English Now, Books 1-5: a complete course in magazine form for the less academic secondary pupil; illustrated in colour.

Twenty-fourth impression 1982   108206
ISBN 0 602 20988 9

Published by Ginn and Company Ltd
Prebendal House, Parson's Fee, Aylesbury, Bucks HP20 2QZ

Printed in Great Britain at the University Press, Cambridge

PREFACE

In Book Four of *Word Perfect Spelling* we have reached a stage in the child's development when the mastery of spelling rules may reasonably be expected to help in forming correct spelling habits. All the simpler rules have, therefore, been included, though much of the work still achieves its object less formally.

As with the earlier books, words and patterns are kept in constant revision, while new patterns, subjects and rules are introduced at a steady rate. Ample scope is also provided for prepared dictation, the importance of which at this stage is increasing. But, since it avails little to be able to spell a word if its meaning is unknown, as the words become more difficult, greater emphasis is now placed upon the understanding of their meaning and usage.

For complete alphabetical word lists and a more detailed discussion of the theory and practice of this spelling course, the teacher is referred to the Teachers' Manual of *Word Perfect Spelling*. In the meantime it may be useful to give some idea of the main points.

The Introductory and eight main books of *Word Perfect Spelling* provide a systematic course in spelling and vocabulary from the ages of 6 or 7 to 15+. Though in the first place it is correct spelling that they aim at, the books will at the same time help the pupil to gain complete mastery over the fundamental vocabularly needed by him at the various stages of his career.

Research has shown beyond dispute that the grouping of words in short lists according to common structural elements does facilitate their learning. The fact that words are held in the mind in certain patterns will, in both the short and the long run, enable them to be recalled more surely. In addition, it allows one key word to be used for unlocking many more. This, then, in the main, is the approach adopted, though other approaches have been used whenever they seemed to have a special contribution to make.

The course, however, does not end with the listing of words: it only begins there. The words have to be linked with the child's interests and brought to life by challenging activities. These activities are in themselves valuable aids to the teaching of English, but they have a vital function in improving spelling. They are based on the self-help principle whereby the pupil can hardly fail to get the right answer. This ensures that he will spell the word correctly when he writes it, and also use it correctly, so gaining the maximum benefit. For a child learns by doing, but he learns much more effectively by doing correctly.

A set of diagnostic tests has been added to the *Teacher's Manual*, thus providing the teacher with a ready means of gauging the point at which any particular child or group should join the *Word Perfect Spelling* course.

Haslemere, 1976 — R.R.

MON
TUES
12
100
?

table	lawn	pilot	paper
chairs	roses	airliner	stories
carpet	lilies	engine	teacher
people	daisies	runway	children
eight	cheese	monkey	bread
twelve	matches	lion	potatoes
twenty	biscuits	tiger	carrots
hundred	toothpaste	elephant	pudding
beak	words	Sunday	toffees
claws	sentences	Monday	chocolates
eyes	questions	Tuesday	packets
feathers	answers	Wednesday	money

These are words that you have met before. Can you still spell them? Write the group of four most likely to be found:

1. in a garden
2. in an English book
3. on a calendar
4. at a sweet shop
5. at the grocer's
6. at an airport
7. in a living-room
8. at the zoo
9. in an Arithmetic book
10. in a classroom
11. on a bird
12. on the dinner table

Use a dictionary to check your spelling as you make your own lists of four things you might find:

13. in your bedroom
14. at the seaside
15. at the station
16. on a farm

Mrs Jones knitting	Andrew diving
Helen dancing	Keith sliding on the ice
Simon swimming	Margaret wrapping a parcel
Mr Parker digging	George clapping the winner
a pony jumping	Sheila choosing a present
a girl skipping	a toddler paddling
John batting	Richard writing a letter

old Mr Williams smoking his pipe

Using the above phrases, write a sentence about each picture, beginning like this: 1. The first picture shows Sheila choosing a present.

dancing	**swimming**	**jumping**	**Sheila**
diving	**skipping**	**wrapping**	**Keith**
sliding	**knitting**	**choosing**	**Margaret**
writing	**clapping**	**paddling**	**George**

beard	**ground**	**earth**	**depart**
peach	**bough**	**heard**	**report**
heath	**thousand**	**search**	**Robert**
easiest	**should**	**earnest**	**pretend**

high	**field**	**truth**	**church**
brightest	**shield**	**board**	**though**
word	**health**	**laugh**	**heart**
world	**heaviest**	**friend**	**fetch**

Can you still spell these familiar words? Write them in eight groups of four according to whether they end in: 1. th, 2. nd, 3. ch, 4. rd, 5. ld, 6. st, 7. rt, 8. gh.

Write the words from the list that rhyme with:
9. teach 10. sigh 11. Ruth 12. stealth 13. low

Next write the words from the list that are opposites of:
14. hardest 15. dullest 16. low 17. arrive 18. lies

Now write the words that mean the same as:
19. moor 20. tall 21. chum 22. leave 23. hunt

24. Instead of f in fetch write: sk, str, wr.
25. Instead of p in peach write: b, r, t, pr.
26. Instead of th in heath write: l, p, r, t, ve, ter.
27. Instead of sh in should write: c, w.
28. Instead of w in weather write: f, h, l.

aunt	**father**	**grandfather**	**cousin**
uncle	**mother**	**grandmother**	**babies**
nephew	**brother**	**husband**	**parents**
niece	**sister**	**wife**	**children**

Complete each sentence with the right word from the patch.

1. Peter's mother and father are his —.
2. The wife of Mary's father is Mary's —.
3. The husband of Mary's mother is Mary's —.
4. Children under two years are usually called —.
5. The father of my father is my —.
6. The mother of my father is my —.
7. My mother's sister is my —.
8. My mother's brother is my —.
9. The son of my aunt is my —.
10. Margaret is her uncle's —, and Roger is his uncle's —.
11. John's father is the — of John's mother.
12. John's mother is the — of John's father.
13. Robert is Susan's —, and Susan is Robert's —, because they both have the same parents.
14. The plural of child is —.

15. Write the words in the patch in alphabetical order. Remember that if two words begin with the same letter, you must look at the second letter. Thus children comes before cousin, because h comes before o. (Note: grandfather comes before grandmother.)

The first place that I can remember at all well was a large pleasant meadow with a pond of clear water in it. Some shady trees leaned over it, and rushes and water lilies grew at the deep end. On one side we looked over a hedge at a ploughed field. On the other side we looked over a gate at our master's house. (From *Black Beauty* by Anna Sewell.)

field	**pleasant**	**edge**	**plough**
belief	**meadow**	**hedge**	**bough**
believe	**measure**	**bridge**	**water**
piece	**pleasure**	**judge**	**remember**

1. Instead of f in field write: sh, y.
2. Instead of ve in believe write: f, ver, ving, ved.
3. In front of dge write: e, he, we, le, ju, bu, ba, do.
4. Instead of m in measure write: pl, tr.
5. Write remember without the prefix re.
6. Instead of p in piece write: n.
7. Write the singular (one only) of: lilies, cities, pennies.

Cut them on Monday, you
cut them for health;
Cut them on Tuesday, you
cut them for wealth;
Cut them on Wednesday,
you cut them for news;
Cut them on Thursday, a new pair of shoes;
Cut them on Friday, you cut them for sorrow;
Cut them on Saturday, see your true love tomorrow;
Cut them on Sunday, ill luck be with you all the week.

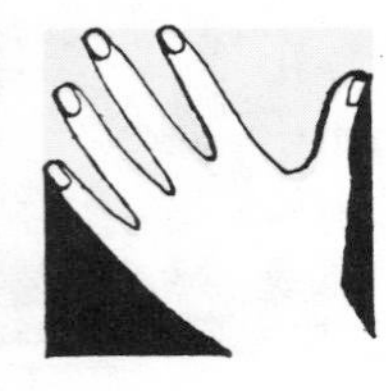

Monday	**Friday**	**wealth**	**sorrow**
Tuesday	**Saturday**	**wealthy**	**borrow**
Wednesday	**Sunday**	**healthy**	**tomorrow**
Thursday	**untrue**	**unhealthy**	**narrow**

One way of making the opposite of a word is to put the prefix un – in front of it. This means not. Thus untrue means not true, and is the opposite of true. Similarly unhealthy is the opposite of healthy and unsafe is the opposite of safe.

By using the prefix un– make the opposites of these words:

1. true	5. dressed	9. even	13. healthy	17. sound
2. wise	6. closed	10. level	14. pleasant	18. seen
3. kind	7. covered	11. alike	15. happy	19. afraid
4. clean	8. tied	12. known	16. common	20. eaten

love	**loving**	**lovely**	**bravery**
hope	**hoping**	**hopeful**	**peaceful**
brave	**braver**	**bravely**	**ripeness**
taste	**tasty**	**tasteless**	**paddler**
meddle	**meddling**	**meddlesome**	**famous**

When you add a suffix to a word ending in a single e, you must drop the e if the suffix begins with a vowel (a, e, i, o, u). Thus it is: use — using — used.

But if the suffix begins with a consonant (any other letter), you must keep the e. Thus it is: use — useful — useless.

Notice that if the suffix is y, it counts as a vowel. Thus it is: stone — stony; taste — tasty.

Make new words by adding –ing to these verbs:
1. taste 2. waste 3. have 4. live 5. stare 6. glance

Make adverbs by adding –ly to these adjectives:
7. safe 8. nice 9. false 10. square 11. wise 12. purpose

Make nouns by adding the suffix –er to these verbs:
13. love 14. move 15. waste 16. make 17. bake 18. tease

Make adjectives by adding –y to these nouns:
19. taste 20. haste 21. breeze 22. chance 23. craze 24. bone

Make adjectives by adding –ful to these nouns:
25. peace 26. care 27. use 28. grace 29. waste 30. spite

Make new words by adding –ous, –less or –able to these:
31. hope 32. fame 33. nerve 34. move 35. care 36. love

Maureen my sister and I fell out,
And what do you think it was all about ?
She loved coffee and I loved tea,
And that was the reason we couldn't agree.

agree	**couldn't**	**reason**	**lovable**
coffee	**wouldn't**	**season**	**agreeable**
referee	**didn't**	**reasonable**	**beautiful**
Maureen	**won't**	**unbeatable**	**treason**

Read the rule on page 7, and then make adjectives by adding –able to these verbs :

1. reason	3. agree	5. love	7. use	9. desire
2. remark	4. disagree	6. like	8. cure	10. obtain

The apostrophe (') may mean that a letter has been left out, or perhaps several letters have been left out. Thus couldn't stands for could not and I'd for I would. Now pair each of these with its full meaning :

11. it's	who is	19. don't	shall not
12. here's	there will	20. won't	it was
13. who's	I am	21. shan't	I would
14. they're	we are	22. hasn't	would not
15. there'll	you have	23. wouldn't	do not
16. you've	it is	24. you'd	has not
17. I'm	they are	25. I'd	you had
18. we're	here is	26. 'twas	will not

Our master was a good, kind man. He gave us good food, good lodging and kind words. He spoke as kindly to us as he did to his little children. We were all fond of him, and my mother loved him dearly. When she saw him by the gate, she would neigh and trot joyfully up to him. He would stroke her and say merrily, "Well, old pet, and how is your little Darkie?" He called me Darkie because I was a dull black colour. I think we were his favourites. (From *Black Beauty* by Anna Sewell.)

joyful	**merry**	**colour**	**neigh**
joyfully	**merrily**	**favour**	**weigh**
tidy	**easy**	**favourite**	**lodging**
tidily	**easily**	**favourable**	**flavour**

Notice that to add –ly to a word ending in y, you must first change the y into i and then add –ly. Now make adverbs by adding –ly to these adjectives:

1. easy	4. nasty	7. joyful	10. weary
2. sudden	5. steady	8. busy	11. greedy
3. merry	6. noisy	9. careful	12. beautiful

January	**first**	**July**	**seventh**
February	**second**	**August**	**eighth**
March	**third**	**September**	**ninth**
April	**fourth**	**October**	**tenth**
May	**fifth**	**November**	**eleventh**
June	**sixth**	**December**	**twelfth**

Write twelve sentences, beginning like this: 1. January is the first month. 2. February is the second month.

Thirty days hath September,
April, June and November.
All the rest have thirty-one,
Excepting February alone,
And that has twenty-eight days clear
And twenty-nine in each leap year.

Write these sentences, putting in the missing words:

13. — usually has twenty-eight days.
14. Every fourth year February has — days.
15. August always has — days.
16. — is the first and — is the last month of the year.
17. The month between July and September is —.
18. The four months ending in y are —, —, — and —.
19. April, —, — and — all have thirty days.
20. January, —, —, —, —, — and — have thirty-one days.

door	**window**	**dwelling**	**larder**
path	**chimney**	**gutter**	**garden**
roof	**drainpipe**	**passage**	**kitchen**
porch	**building**	**garage**	**entrance**

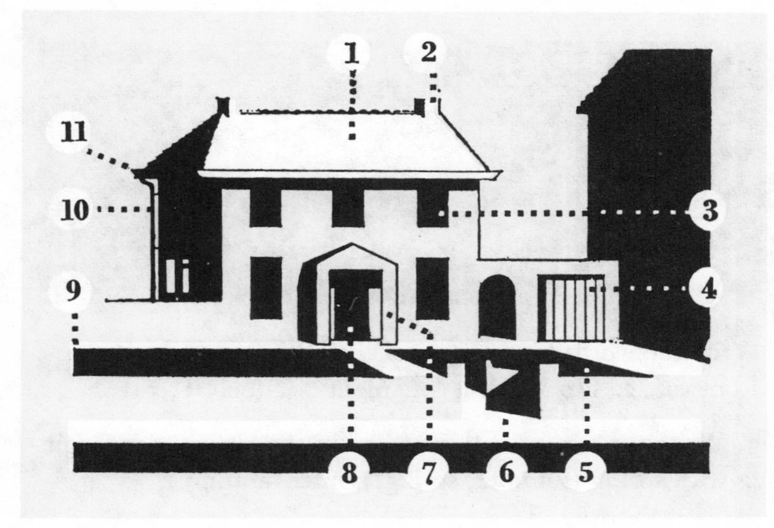

Write the numbers 1–11 and put the right name beside each.

12. Instead of d in door write: p, fl, m.
13. Instead of dw in dwelling write: t, sp, sw.
14. Instead of p in porch write: t, sc.
15. Instead of g in gutter write: b, c, m, sh, fl, st, spl.
16. Instead of gar in garage write: w, st, pass, post, sav, saus, dam, man, mess, voy, band, pack, cour, cott.

Good King Wenceslas looked out
On the Feast of Stephen,
When the snow lay round about
Deep and crisp and even.
Brightly shone the moon that night,
Though the frost was cruel,
When a poor man came in sight,
Gathering winter fuel.

fuel	**even**	**shone**	**turkey**
cruel	**event**	**chicken**	**holly**
cruet	**evening**	**sausages**	**pudding**
Stephen	**gathering**	**Christmas**	**stuffing**

Write the words from the carol that rhyme with:
1. beast 2. lisp 3. lost 4. night 5. fuel 6. Stephen

7. Write the names of the seasons in the right order, beginning with spring (summer, spring, winter, autumn).

Arrange each of these lists in alphabetical order:

8.	9.	10.	11.
dinner	feast	Stephen	crackers
supper	crisp	Christopher	jellies
stuffing	carol	Catherine	berries
breakfast	even	George	evenings
sausages	gather	Gordon	turkeys
seasoning	frosty	Philip	geese
goose	fuel	Percy	children

PAGE THIRTEEN (13)

1. b _ _ _ _ _ This goes across a river. (page 5)
2. _ _ s _ e _ _ _ _ Without any taste. (7)
3. _ _ _ r u _ _ _ The second month of the year. (10)
4. _ _ _ p h _ _ _ Largest land animal in the world. (1)
5. _ _ _ _ e _ The plural of baby. (4)
6. _ _ _ _ v _ A dozen. (1)
7. _ w _ _ _ _ _ _ Moving through the water. (2)
8. _ _ _ _ t _ Next after the seventh. (10)
9. _ _ d d _ _ _ _ Moving feet about in the water. (2)
10. _ _ i e _ _ The opposite of enemy. (3)
11. _ _ u _ _ The opposite of kind. (12)
12. _ _ e _ _ A girl is this to her uncle. (4)
13. _ e _ _ _ _ _ _ The opposite of to forget. (5)
14. _ _ _ o _ _ Very well known. (7)
15. _ e _ _ _ _ _ The opposite of poor. (6)
16. _ _ r _ _ _ House for a car. (11)
17. _ _ u _ _ _ _ _ Chopped meat stuffed into tubes. (12)
18. _ o _ _ _ _ _ _ The day after today. (6)
19. _ n _ _ _ _ _ _ _ _ Not able to be beaten. (8)
20. _ _ _ _ _ The cry of a horse. (9)
21. _ _ _ _ _ _ _ _ _ Possessing beauty. (8)
22. _ _ _ _ _ _ _ _ _ The day between Tuesday and Thursday. (6)
23. _ _ _ _ _ _ The opposite of to arrive. (3)
24. _ _ _ _ _ _ This is used to turn over soil. (5)
25. _ _ _ _ _ _ More brave. (7)
26. _ _ _ _ _ _ _ Judge of play in a game. (8)
27. _ _ _ _ _ _ _ _ _ The one liked better than the others. (9)

Test yourself

(1)

able	**listen**	**Peter**	**pitch**
table	**hasten**	**Mary**	**stretch**
capable	**often**	**Michael**	**catch**
lovable	**dozen**	**Margaret**	**scratch**

(2)

stare	**salt**	**ticket**	**sugar**
spare	**alter**	**bucket**	**potatoes**
share	**chalk**	**size**	**chocolates**
daring	**stalk**	**prize**	**biscuits**

(3)

fleet	**skipping**	**niece**	**rule**
queer	**paddling**	**piece**	**ruler**
greedy	**knitting**	**shield**	**loser**
freedom	**wrapping**	**believe**	**lover**

For dictation

The story called "Black Beauty" was written about a hundred years ago. Anna Sewell wrote it because she was fond of horses. She pretended that the horse was telling his own story. In this way she tried to make people understand horses better. She hoped that they would then look after them well and never be cruel to them. It became very famous and is still read by thousands of children every year.

dislike	**repeat**	**delay**	**expand**
disgrace	**remain**	**depend**	**express**
discuss	**refuse**	**demand**	**expense**
disgust	**reserve**	**deliver**	**excite**

Make new words by putting re– in front of these:

1. new 2. mind 3. pair 4. mark 5. move 6. cover

Make new words by putting the prefix ex– in front of these:

7. change 8. claim 9. it 10. plain 11. port

Make new words by adding the prefix dis– to these:

12. grace 13. cover 14. like 15. please 16. miss

Make new words by adding the prefix re– to these:

17. turn 18. ward 19. tire 20. quest 21. verse

Make new words by adding the prefix be– to these:

22. come 23. long 24. low 25. side 26. ware

There are two syllables in refuse (re-fuse). Show the two syllables in each of these words:

27. express 29. exact 31. review 33. behave
28. discuss 30. demand 32. betray 34. exchange

There are three syllables in disorder (dis-or-der). Show the three syllables in each of these words:

35. reorder 37. disgusting 39. deliver 41. exciting
36. discover 38. disgraceful 40. repeated 42. expensive

Make new words using one of these: re–, ex–, dis–, de–.

43. part 44. tent 45. able 46. late 47. trust 48. serve

inform	**confuse**	**excuse**	**platform**
intend	**conduct**	**except**	**perform**
inquire	**content**	**permit**	**giant**
interest	**concert**	**admit**	**servant**

Make the words asked for from the syllables in the boxes:

Syllables	Clues
mit ad per	1. to allow 2. to let in
form per in	3. to act in public 4. to supply with facts
ant gi serv	5. huge imaginary man 6. person employed by another
con fuse cert	7. musical entertainment 8. to mix up or bewilder
cuse ex cept	9. a reason or explanation for 10. leaving out
duct tent con	11. satisfied 12. to lead or guide

Confusing is made up of three syllables (con – fus – ing). Split each of these into three syllables:

13. conducting	17. pretended	21. interest
14. performing	18. conducted	22. excuses
15. excusing	19. disgraceful	23. conductor
16. contented	20. repeated	24. inquiry

Sometimes a rough boy called Dick would come into our field to pick blackberries. When he had eaten all he wanted, he would have what he called fun with the colts. He threw sticks and stones at them to make them gallop. We did not mind very much because we could gallop away. But sometimes a stone would hit us and hurt us.

One morning he played this game and did not know that the master was in the next field watching. He scrambled over the hedge and caught Dick in the act.

"You are a naughty boy to chase the colts," he grumbled. "That will be quite enough. I never want to see you on my farm again." (From *Black Beauty* by Anna Sewell.)

caught	**gallop**	**rough**	**scramble**
taught	**carrot**	**enough**	**grumble**
naughty	**ribbon**	**tough**	**bundle**
daughter	**cotton**	**morning**	**bangle**

1. Instead of b in bangle write: d, m, t.
2. Instead of gr in grumble write: h, m, t, j, f, r, st.
3. Instead of co in cotton write: mu, bu, glu.
4. Instead of c in carrot write: p.
5. Instead of scr in scramble write: g, r, br.
6. Instead of op in gallop write: ant, ey, on, ows.

sailor	**major**	**senior**	**size**
tailor	**motor**	**junior**	**gaze**
actor	**doctor**	**visitor**	**gazing**
tractor	**author**	**monitor**	**razor**

To complete these sentences correctly, use each word from the patch once only.

1. An — performs on the stage.
2. A person who writes books is called an —.
3. A — makes clothes.
4. Major Senior uses a — to shave off his beard.

5 Robert takes — three in shoes.
6. The — in my class looks after the library books.
7. The farmer uses a — to pull his plough.
8. The — in charge of a ship is called the captain.

9. The word — means the opposite of minor, but it may also mean an army officer.
10. — rhymes with craze and means to look hard.
11. A — school takes pupils from 7 to 11.
12. — pupils, aged 11 upwards, go to secondary schools.

13. Anyone who calls to see you at your house is a —.
14. When Mr Lazy grew too fat he had to go to see a —.
15. Any engine used to drive a machine is called a —.
16. Having finished, he sat — at his beautiful work.

ankle	**forehead**
ear	**finger**
elbow	**wrist**
thigh	**eyebrow**
calf	**mouth**
palm	**shoulder**
knee	**stomach**
thumb	**nose**

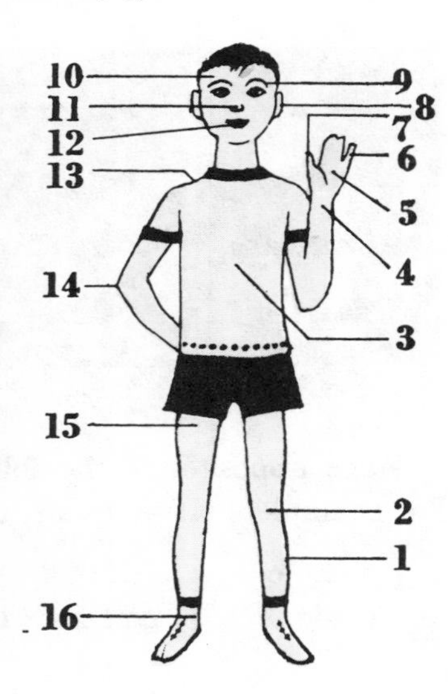

Write the names in the same order as the numbers (1–16).

Write the words that rhyme with:

17. south 18. half 19. twist 20. calm 21. boulder 22. sigh 23. toes 24. come

Write the adjectives from which these adverbs have been formed. E.g. merrily is formed from merry.

25. merrily 26. angrily 27. hungrily 28. wearily 29. ably 30. gently 31. beautifully 32. capably

Write the adverbs that can be formed from these adjectives:

33. happy 34. hasty 35. careful 36. hopeful 37. simple 38. feeble 39. horrible 40. reliable

obey	**expect**	**Britain**	**discover**
disobey	**respect**	**certain**	**contain**
advantage	**disrespect**	**fountain**	**damaged**
disadvantage	**respectful**	**mountain**	**protect**

Make opposites of the following by using the prefix un–. For example: safe—unsafe, tied—untied.

1. able	3. selfish	5. cover	7. expected
2. done	4. certain	6. damaged	8. protected

Make opposites of these by using the prefix dis–.

9. obey	12. grace	15. agree	18. cover
10. trust	13. like	16. pleased	19. advantage
11. mount	14. appear	17. respect	20. respectful

Break into syllables each word in the patch, beginning like this: 21. o – bey, 22. dis – o – bey. There are ten with two syllables, five with three, and one with four.

37. Instead of cer in <u>certain</u> write: cur, con, s, cap, ob.
38. Instead of dam in <u>damage</u> write: sav, voy, man, pass.

Notice these: waste—wasteful—wastefully. Make a similar series from each of these:

39. care	41. faith	43. cheer	45. beauty	47. disgrace
40. truth	42. joy	44. use	46. mercy	48. plenty

I shall never forget the first train that ran by. I was feeding quietly near the fence that separates the field from the railway, when I heard a strange sound in the distance. With a rush and a clatter, a long black thing flew past, and was gone almost before I could draw my breath. I turned and galloped to the other side of the field. During the day many more trains went by. Some drew up at the station close by, making an awful shriek before they stopped. At first I thought they were dreadful. But as these terrible monsters never came into the field or did me any harm, I soon began to ignore them. (Adapted from *Black Beauty* by Anna Sewell.)

nation	**breath**	**strange**	**monster**
station	**awful**	**stranger**	**shriek**
motion	**clatter**	**danger**	**separate**
mention	**terrible**	**distance**	**ignore**

Fill the gaps with the right words from the patch.

1. When you draw your — you take air into your lungs.
2. A — is a place where trains stop.
3. To — something is to take no notice of it.
4. A — is a huge thing that frightens you.
5. A loud sharp noise is called a —.
6. To — means to keep apart.

novel	**manage**	**porter**	**carpenter**
novelist	**manager**	**grocer**	**passenger**
cycle	**travel**	**artist**	**explorer**
cyclist	**traveller**	**typist**	**bricklayer**

1. Cyclist, typist, explorer, manager are formed from: cycle, type, explore, manage. Write out the rule from page 7 that tells you how to form such words.

2. Notice that travel doubles the l before adding –er. In the same way forget doubles the t before adding a suffix beginning with a vowel (forgetting, forgotten), but not before a suffix beginning with a consonant (forgetful). Now add –er to these:

   (*a*) travel (*b*) jewel (*c*) begin (*d*) forget

3. Add –ing to the following:
   (*a*) forget (*b*) begin (*c*) travel (*d*) level (*e*) control

Choose the right words from the patch to complete these:

4. A person who rides a cycle is called a —.
5. Novels are long story books and are written by the —.
6. The — makes and repairs things in wood.
7. Amundsen was the — who first reached the South Pole.
8. A — writes letters on a typewriter.
9. The person who sits by the driver is his —.
10. A — is a person who is in charge of a shop or office.

knife	**wrap**	**weigh**	**thumb**
knuckle	**wrist**	**weight**	**crumb**
knead	**whole**	**eighty**	**doubt**
knowledge	**sword**	**height**	**debt**

1. Which is the silent letter or letters in each group above?
2. Rewrite the following in four groups in the same way:

frighten	climbed	wrapping	wholly
written	fought	eighth	knock
knives	although	doubter	bomber
knotted	knitting	combing	wreck

How would you arrange the first list in the patch in alphabetical order? If the first two letters of any two words are the same, we must look at the third letters. Thus knead will come before knife, because e comes before i. Similarly knife will come before knowledge because i comes before o. And so on. Now arrange the following in alphabetical order:

3. the first list in the patch
4. the second list in the patch
5. the first list in the ring
6. knob, knit, knead, knuckle, knack
7. whom, wrapper, wringer, wreckage, white, whole
8. dumb, debt, delight, deaf, demand, doubt, deny, depart

islands	**loaves**	**factories**	**potatoes**
yachts	**thieves**	**difficulties**	**tomatoes**
churches	**chiefs**	**libraries**	**pianos**
stitches	**dwarfs**	**railways**	**geese**

Remember that singular means one only, and plural means more than one. Remember also that a, e, i, o, u are vowels and all the other letters of the alphabet are consonants.

Rules for forming the plural

1. The usual way to form the plural of a noun is to add –s to the singular. E.g. carpet—carpets, island—islands.
2. But nouns ending in a hissing sound (s, sh, ch, x, z) add –es. E.g. dress—dresses, church—churches.
3. Some ending in f change the f to v and then add –es. E.g. loaf—loaves, shelf—shelves.
4. A few ending in f simply add –s. E.g. roofs, cliffs, chiefs.
5. If the noun ends in y with a consonant before it, you must change the y into i and then add –es. E.g. lady—ladies, factory—factories.
6. But if the noun ends in y with a vowel before it, you simply add –s. E.g. valley—valleys, railway—railways.
7. Some ending in o add –es. E.g. potatoes, mottoes.
8. Others ending in o simply add –s. E.g. pianos, Eskimos.
9. Some are irregular. E.g. mouse—mice, woman—women.

heroes	**crows**	**solos**	**hoofs**	**monkeys**
negroes	**swallows**	**pianos**	**cliffs**	**chimneys**
cargoes	**sparrows**	**banjos**	**gulfs**	**valleys**
firemen	**babies**	**witches**	**wives**	—
children	**injuries**	**glasses**	**leaves**	—
teeth	**pennies**	**wishes**	**halves**	—

Each group has formed its plural according to one of the rules on page 24. Write the groups in the same order as the rules, numbering them, like the rules, 1–9.

Number 10 has formed its plural according to rule 1; number 11 according to rule 2, and so on. Write out the singular forms:

10. robins
11. atlases
12. knives
13. scarfs
14. daisies
15. runways
16. volcanoes
17. Eskimos
18. women

The ways in which these nouns form their plurals are also in the same order as the rules. Write out their plural forms:

19. object
20. branch
21. thief
22. cuff
23. cherry
24. chimney
25. potato
26. solo
27. foot

Rewrite these, changing the italicised nouns to singular:

28. The *thieves* stole *dresses*, *watches*, *knives* and *pianos*.
29. These *firemen* are *heroes* in those *cities*.
30. The *children* were picking *cherries* in the *valleys*.
31. These *shelves* hold *novels*, *atlases* and *plays*.

midnight	**although**	**warmth**	**shepherd**
delightful	**altogether**	**wardrobe**	**popular**
frightful	**welcome**	**warning**	**regular**
already	**fulfil**	**quarter**	**particular**

A red sky at night
Is the shepherd's delight.
A red sky in the morning
Is the shepherd's warning.

The south wind brings wet weather,
The north wind wet and cold together.
The west wind always brings us rain;
The east wind blows it back again.

Here is an extra list of words. They are all common ones that you will need to be able to spell; but they are rather odd, and each one needs learning separately.

vase	**laughter**	**owe**	**several**
iron	**comfort**	**due**	**worship**
apron	**poetry**	**else**	**ocean**
union	**diary**	**ache**	**wander**

PAGE TWENTY-SEVEN (27)

1. _ _ _ _ o r A person who writes books. (page 18)
2. e x _ _ _ _ To grow bigger. (15)
3. _ y _ _ _ _ _ Anyone who rides a cycle. (22)
4. _ _ _ _ _ s s To talk over. (15)
5. _ _ _ _ a _ To say again. (15)
6. _ _ _ _ _ k A loud sharp noise. (21)
7. _ _ _ _ i _ _ A stopping place for trains. (21)
8. _ _ _ c _ _ _ A musical entertainment. (16)
9. _ _ _ v _ _ _ Any person employed by another. (16)
10. _ _ _ a _ To mix by pressing and squeezing. (23)
11. _ _ _ _ o _ To run fast like a horse. (17)
12. _ _ _ g _ The opposite of tender. (17)
13. _ _ _ _ r The opposite of minor. (18)
14. _ _ z _ _ Sharp tool to shave with. (18)
15. _ _ _ _ _ _ _ e _ The plural of library. (24)
16. _ _ _ _ t The part between hand and arm. (19)
17. _ _ _ _ The inside of the hand. (19)
18. _ _ _ _ _ _ _ _ The plural of injury. (25)
19. _ _ _ _ _ _ _ The opposite of to obey. (20)
20. _ _ _ _ _ _ _ The opposite of doubtful. (20)
21. _ _ _ _ _ _ _ _ _ _ Showing that you look up to someone. (20)
22. _ _ _ _ _ _ Person who uses a typewriter. (22)
23. _ _ _ _ _ _ _ _ To keep apart. (21)
24. _ _ _ _ _ _ To take no notice of. (21)
25. _ _ _ _ Something owed to another. (23)
26. _ _ _ _ _ Lack of belief or sureness. (23)
27. _ _ _ _ _ _ Light sailing boats for racing. (24)

PAGE TWENTY-EIGHT (28)

Test yourself

(1)

children	**nation**	**wrong**	**mountain**
women	**station**	**among**	**country**
piece	**question**	**across**	**France**
shriek	**dictation**	**avoid**	**advance**

(2)

excuse	**worry**	**extra**	**curtain**
refuse	**carry**	**except**	**certain**
pure	**carrot**	**excite**	**obtain**
picture	**barrow**	**explain**	**captain**

(3)

terrible	**protect**	**disagree**	**people**
horrible	**respectful**	**disadvantage**	**beautiful**
traveller	**merciful**	**disgusting**	**sausages**
beginner	**unhappily**	**disgraceful**	**chimney**

For dictation

One night a terrible thing happened. The stable containing Black Beauty and several other horses caught on fire. The horses became very excited. They trembled all over. They were so frightened that they refused to leave the building. It seemed as if they would all be burned alive. Then James, the groom, fought his way through the smoke and flames. He tied his scarf over the eyes of Black Beauty, spoke to him gently and led him out into the yard.

square	**bowl**	**burn**	**declare**
beware	**growth**	**furnish**	**Glasgow**
compare	**pillow**	**murder**	**purpose**
prepare	**follow**	**purple**	**surprise**

1. Instead of n in burn write: st, ner, ning, den, glar.
2. Instead of th in growth write: n, ing, er, l.
3. Instead of pi in pillow write: fo, ho, ye, fe, sha, swa.
4. Instead of pose in purpose write: ple, se, chase, sue.
5. Instead of prise in surprise write: name, round, mount.
6. Instead of fur in furnish write: fi, pu, var, Spa.
7. Write the five words in the patch that rhyme with dare.

Read the rule on page 7. Then add –ing and –ed to these:

8. prepare	10. murder	12. compare	14. surround
9. follow	11. surprise	13. furnish	15. glare

Pair each numbered word with its opposite.

16. follow	reckless	24. dwarfs	straight
17. finish	deep	25. curse	together
18. careful	lead	26. curly	bless
19. shallow	common	27. pursue	unready
20. vanish	peace	28. separate	lead
21. rare	begin	29. further	giants
22. warfare	sell	30. prepared	ignorance
23. purchase	appear	31. knowledge	nearer

stoop	**labour**	**huge**	**journey**
smooth	**harbour**	**amuse**	**armour**
loose	**humour**	**future**	**kangaroo**
choose	**honour**	**introduce**	**usual**

Write the words from the patch that mean the opposite of:

1. tiny 2. past 3. rough 4. firm 5. dishonour

Now write the words that mean the same as:

6. work 7. entertain 8. vast 9. voyage 10. elect

11. Write the nine words from the patch that can be made from this sentence, using each letter once only in any one word:

MANY YACHTS SAILED INTO THE HARBOUR

Write the plurals of these words:

12. harbour	14. pillow	16. injury	18. kangaroo
13. journey	15. goose	17. diary	19. guess

Pair each numbered word with its synonym (word of same meaning):

20. loose	judge	28. often	rarely
21. huge	pursue	29. seldom	burglars
22. choose	wobbly	30. careless	frequently
23. referee	entertainment	31. vanish	purchase
24. usual	gigantic	32. buy	burden
25. follow	uncommon	33. thieves	unusual
26. rare	ordinary	34. strange	disappear
27. amusement	select	35. weight	reckless

The Wright brothers were famous American airmen. In the beginning they made only gliders. Then one day they had the brilliant idea of fixing an engine to one of the gliders. The engine drove a propeller at the rear of the aeroplane.

When everything was ready, they took their machine to the top of a hill. The engine roared, and the machine gathered speed. At last it rose into the air and travelled a few hundred metres at fifty kilometres an hour. It was the first proper aeroplane in the world to fly.

travelled	**engine**	**proper**	**America**
propeller	**machine**	**property**	**American**
beginning	**divide**	**famous**	**Africa**
brilliant	**aeroplane**	**dangerous**	**African**

Fill the gaps with the right words from the patch :

1. A — person is one who is very well known.
2. An — is a flying machine driven by an engine.
3. The engine drives a — that makes the aeroplane fly.
4. An — is a person from the United States of America.
5. An — is a person from Africa.
6. — means very bright or very clever.
7. The start means the same as the —.
8. The things belonging to a person are called his —.

towel	**tempt**	**silent**	**parcel**
vowel	**empty**	**silence**	**prompt**
label	**empties**	**absent**	**tenpence**
model	**attempt**	**absence**	**parent**

1. Instead of p in pence write: f, h, sil, abs, lic, def, sci, viol, differ, excell.

The noun silence is formed from the adjective silent. Form nouns in the same way from these adjectives:

2. absent 3. present 4. violent 5. different

Write the plural of these nouns:

6. label 7. towel 8. rebel 9. party 10. country

11. Write these in alphabetical order: silence, science, defence, duties, difference, promptly, parcel.

12. Solve this crossword puzzle:

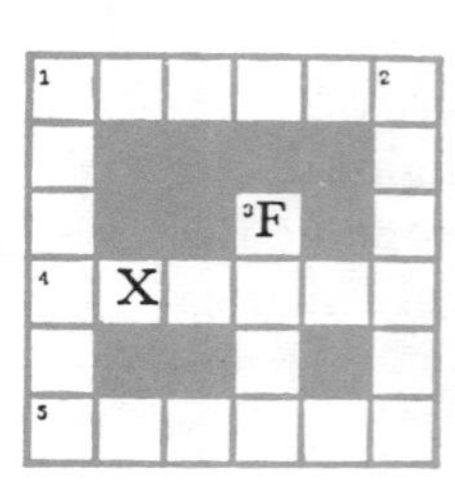

Across

1. A package wrapped in paper.
4. A reason or explanation for something.
5. Cloths with which to dry yourself.

Down

1. Mother or father.
2. These tell what is inside.
3. This breaks, stopping the electricity.

Doctor	**Captain**	**London**	**McDonald**
Major	**Sergeant**	**Belfast**	**O'Brien**
Lord	**Corporal**	**Birmingham**	**Johnson**
Taylor	**Reverend**	**Manchester**	**Robinson**

When we place the names of people in alphabetical order, the titles do not count. We decide the order by the surname. The Christian names or initials do not count either, unless the surnames are the same. Thus Eric Jones will come before Ronald Jones because E comes before R. In the same way, B. R. McDonald comes before B. T. McDonald, because R comes before T.

Now place each of these groups in alphabetical order:

1. Miss Davies, Mrs Evans, Mr Morgan, Capt. Jones.
2. E. Johnson, Don Robinson, G. Baker, Tom Hopkinson.
3. Sir James Adams, Lord McDonald, The Rev. E. Taylor, Capt. Cross, Miss Horner, Dr White, Mrs Gilbert.
4. Hunter, Lewis, O'Brien, Hughes, Lodge, Lamb, Hinks.
5. Bishop, Allen, Barber, Knight, Scott, Shaw, Stanley.
6. James Parker, Colin Morris, C. R. Davies, John Thomas, C. T. Derby, Sue Stephenson, N. Patrick, Flora Macdonald.
7. Liverpool, Manchester, London, Belfast, Dublin, York, Dover, Derby, Glasgow, Cardiff, Swansea, Bristol, Bradford.
8. Maj. E. Douglas, Miss B. W. Stewart, Col. A. Wilson, Sergt. Jones, Mrs S. B. Johnson, Mr C. T. M. Smith, Capt. A. Walker, Lord Woolton.

stern	**defeat**	**reply**	**Germany**
modern	**desire**	**apply**	**applied**
govern	**defy**	**hurry**	**applying**
desert	**deny**	**occupy**	**behaving**

Make new words by adding:

1. –ly to stern
2. –ment to govern
3. –est to stern
4. –ing to govern
5. –ed to defend
6. –er to desert

Read the rule on page 7, and then make new words by adding –ing and –ed to each of these verbs:

7. desire
8. behave
9. inquire
10. invite
11. escape
12. chuckle
13. stare
14. huddle

Make new words by adding –ful, –less, –ing, –ed to each of:

15. use
16. care
17. help
18. taste
19. doubt

When you add a suffix to a word ending in y which has a consonant before it, you must change the y into i, except before i. E.g. carry—carried—carrying—carrier; pray—praying—prayed—prayer.

Now add –ing and –ed to each of these verbs:

20. apply
21. reply
22. hurry
23. occupy
24. defy
25. deny
26. copy
27. bury
28. pray
29. play

Write the short words ending in y from which these come:

30. occupies
31. replied
32. tried
33. supplies
34. satisfies
35. cried
36. copies
37. earlier
38. prettier
39. pitiful
40. liveliness
41. daintiest

said	**cried**	**remarked**	**bellowed**
asked	**replied**	**demanded**	**thundered**
thought	**shouted**	**wondered**	**inquired**
laughed	**whispered**	**answered**	**chuckled**

After each question write the correct answer from below:

1. " Where are you going ? " asked Margaret.
2. " May I have another helping ? " asked Keith.
3. " Is the water cold ? " cried John.
4. " Why are you picking those apples ? " thundered the farmer.
5. " Is it far to the station ? " inquired the woman.

" It's almost freezing," shouted back George.
" No, it's just round the corner," answered the postman.
" I am sorry, but there is no more left," said his father.
" I am going shopping," replied her mother.
" Your wife asked me to," chuckled Ronald.

For dictation

(*a*) "What is the noun formed from absent?" asked Miss Lake.
(*b*) "It is absence", answered Margaret.

(*c*) " Why have you locked the gate ? " inquired the visitor.
(*d*) " If I didn't lock it, the pony would push it open," laughed the farmer.

(*e*) " Which is the largest city in the world ? " demanded the teacher.
(*f*) " Tokyo is," replied Andrew.

England	**English**	**vanish**	**establish**
Scotland	**Scottish**	**polish**	**escape**
Wales	**Welsh**	**punish**	**estimate**
Ireland	**Irish**	**perish**	**especial**

Arrange each of these groups in alphabetical order:

1. finish, perish, punish, polish, parish, publish
2. escape, esquire, establish, especial, essay
3. Ireland, Spain, Scotland, Africa, America, India
4. Instead of van in vanish write: pol, pun, per, ban, publ, par, establ, Engl, Span, Ir, Corn, Scott.

If we add – ment to punish, we get punishment. Now make new words by adding –ment to the following:

5. amuse	7. pave	9. treat	11. engage
6. move	8. base	10. arrange	12. enjoy

Make new words by adding –ing and –ed to each of these:

13. escape	15. inquire	17. excite	19. confuse	21. graze
14. estimate	16. chuckle	18. refuse	20. excuse	22. damage

Use the suffixes –ment, –less, –ful five times each to make new words from these:

23. wire	26. sense	29. shape	32. spite	35. disgrace
24. move	27. peace	30. cease	33. agree	36. excite
25. pay	28. price	31. grate	34. fright	37. employ

In the early days of flying, a famous airman once found himself surrounded by thick fog. He could not see anywhere, and in those days there were no control towers to guide him to an airfield. Then suddenly the fog cleared and he saw that he was over a town. Just at that moment the engine began to splutter. It had run out of petrol. The pilot steered his machine towards the open country and then baled out. But the danger was not over. As his parachute came down, he noticed that the aeroplane was flying round in circles. If it touched him he would be killed. Luckily, the plane at last crashed in a field and the airman landed safely on the road.

notice	**aeroplane**	**guide**	**circle**
office	**parachute**	**guess**	**suddenly**
officer	**control**	**guard**	**luckily**
surround	**petrol**	**guilty**	**guiltily**

Read the rule on page 34, and then make adverbs by adding –ly to these adjectives:

1. lucky 3. merry 5. weary 7. hearty 9. sudden
2. guilty 4. happy 6. hasty 8. clumsy 10. steady

Make new words by adding:

11. –er to office 13. –ed to circle 15. –ful to mercy
12. –ed to notice 14. –ful to beauty 16. –ness to clumsy

eager	**strive**	**music**	**horrid**
eagle	**arrive**	**public**	**stupid**
appear	**advice**	**limit**	**traffic**
beneath	**police**	**spirit**	**visitor**

Notice that by adding the suffix –ness to an adjective we can make a noun. E.g. eager—eagerness, clumsy—clumsiness. But remember that when the adjective ends in y, you must change the y into i before adding the suffix.

Now make nouns ending in –ness from these adjectives:

1. deaf	4. silly	7. sharp	10. lovely
2. lame	5. tired	8. brief	11. ready
3. ugly	6. scarce	9. early	12. gentle

Make adverbs by adding –ly to these adjectives:

13. eager	15. public	17. rapid	19. gentle
14. timid	16. stern	18. vivid	20. capable

21. Instead of pol in police write: off, not, adv, pr, tw, just.

Write each of these groups in alphabetical order:

22. limit, visit, omit, inhabit, admit, credit, habit
23. rabbit, public, stupid, spirit, permit, rapid
24. defeat, retreat, reader, dearest, beaten, beneath
25. spire, strive, stile, slice, service, tribe, twice
26. timid, traffic, horrid, hearing, tearful, terrific

error	**whisker**	**petal**	**local**
terror	**whisper**	**metal**	**musical**
terrible	**whistle**	**medal**	**terrific**
terrify	**thistle**	**mental**	**castle**

Write the words from the patch that rhyme with:
1. thistle 2. metal 3. terror 4. pedal 5. verify

Make adverbs by adding –ly to each of these adjectives:
6. local 7. mental 8. musical 9. terrible 10. horrible

Make new words by adding:

11. –er to whistle
12. –er to whisper
13. –al to music
14. –ed to horrify
15. –ly to loyal
16. –ness to easy
17. –ing to whistle
18. –ing to terrify
19. –ty to loyal

Write these lists in alphabetical order:

20. terror, horror, hollow, hilly, tunic, marrow, music
21. pedal, petal, mental, metal, medal, loyal, local
22. whistle, thistle, whole, often, soften, castle, cattle

23. This crossword puzzle has been solved. With the help of the definitions below, write out the clues.

[1]P	E	[2]D	A	[3]L
E		I		O
[4]T	U	N	I	C
A		G		A
[5]L	O	Y	A	L

not at all bright and fresh
to do with the place round about
faithful to duty
lever worked by foot
a leaf-like part of a blossom
short coat worn by soldier

Speak roughly to your little boy
  And beat him when he sneezes.
He only does it to annoy
  Because he knows it teases.

I speak severely to my boy.
  I beat him when he sneezes,
For he can thoroughly enjoy
  The pepper when he pleases!

speak	**enjoy**	**pepper**	**sneeze**
please	**annoy**	**bottle**	**breeze**
tease	**enjoyable**	**cunning**	**roughly**
disease	**severely**	**suppose**	**thoroughly**

Notice that when you make the plural of a word like breeze, you simply add –s: breeze—breezes, disease—diseases. But in fact it sounds as if you had added –es. You don't, however, need the e because there is already a silent e at the end of the word. In the plural this silent e is sounded.

Make the plural of these nouns:

1. sneeze	3. house	5. size	7. squeeze	9. crease
2. sense	4. verse	6. craze	8. noise	10. surprise

due	**shriek**	**receive**	**rescue**
value	**priest**	**deceive**	**handkerchief**
argue	**grief**	**conceit**	**deceitful**
avenue	**fierce**	**ceiling**	**relief**

Notice that the ie or ei in the words in the patch is sounded like ee in sweet.

When the sound is like ee, you put i before e, except after c, when it is e before i.

1. Write the following words in two equal lists according to whether they follow the rule or the exception: yield, shield, field, deceit, ceiling, chief, conceive, receive.

Make new words by adding –er to these. (See rule on page 7.)

2. argue	5. receive	8. use	11. believe	14. score
3. rescue	6. deceive	9. rule	12. cure	15. skate
4. value	7. invade	10. tease	13. manage	16. sparkle

Make the comparative and superlative forms of these adjectives. E.g. fiercer, fiercest.

17. fierce	19. rare	21. true	23. sure	25. thin
18. scarce	20. late	22. brave	24. gentle	26. big

Make new words by adding a prefix (re–, un–, dis–) and a suffix (–ness, –ment, –er, –ful) to each of these:

27. late 28. sure 29. agree 30. believe 31. respect

1. _ _ _ _ s h To make brighter. (page 36)
2. _ _ _ p _ _ _ To get ready. (29)
3. _ _ _ l _ _ The opposite of to lead. (29)
4. _ e _ _ _ _ To say again. (15)
5. _ _ o o _ _ To pick out or select. (30)
6. _ _ _ _ _ u _ Place of shelter for ships. (30)
7. _ _ _ _ u _ Very well known. (7)
8. _ _ _ _ _ _ _ u _ Full of danger. (31)
9. _ e _ _ _ _ _ _ _ Power-driven flying machine. (31)
10. _ _ _ _ _ e _ Hole by which smoke escapes. (11)
11. _ _ _ _ e _ Package wrapped in paper. (32)
12. e _ _ _ _ The opposite of full. (32)
13. _ _ _ _ _ e Ring worn around wrist. (17)
14. _ _ _ _ e _ _ _ Army rank just above corporal. (33)
15. _ _ e _ _ _ _ Next after eleventh. (10)
16. _ e _ _ To resist boldly or openly. (34)
17. _ _ _ e _ _ The opposite of old-fashioned. (34)
18. _ _ _ _ _ _ e _ The plural of stitch. (24)
19. _ _ _ _ _ _ _ e _ Spoke very softly. (35)
20. _ _ _ _ _ e To get free. (36)
21. _ e _ _ _ _ _ _ _ Possessing beauty. (8)
22. _ _ _ _ _ _ The opposite of innocent. (37)
23. _ _ _ _ _ _ The opposite of depart. (38)
24. _ _ _ _ _ _ _ Vehicles coming and going in street. (38)
25. _ _ _ _ _ _ Fortified building of the past. (39)
26. _ _ _ _ _ _ _ _ _ _ Completely. (40)
27. _ _ _ _ _ _ Road with trees on both sides. (41)
28. _ _ _ _ _ _ _ Inside top covering of a room. (41)

Test yourself

(1)

towel	**idle**	**expect**	**fuel**
level	**noble**	**respect**	**cruel**
bushel	**uncle**	**inspect**	**picture**
angel	**title**	**insect**	**adventure**

(2)

death	**dozen**	**extra**	**fruit**
threat	**oven**	**excuse**	**orange**
instead	**linen**	**excellent**	**apple**
dreadful	**listen**	**except**	**strawberry**

(3)

naughty	**music**	**people**	**petrol**
daughter	**picnic**	**honest**	**engine**
certain	**pleasant**	**wicked**	**machine**
entertain	**treasure**	**amusing**	**factory**

For dictation

Margaret thought she was an excellent artist, but her brother was not so certain. One morning she was putting the finishing touches to a picture of a house.

" I am trying to think of a title for my new painting," she informed her brother. " Have you any ideas ? "

John looked at the picture very thoroughly. " Why not call it Home ? " he replied after a while.

" But why Home ? " inquired Margaret.

" Well, there's no place like it," explained her brother.

For extra work

(1)

bullet	vessel	nature	fortune
bonnet	funnel	figure	fortunate
mirror	channel	endure	continue
woollen	barrel	creature	continuation

(2)

mercy	attend	account	complete
fancy	attack	afford	compete
study	address	occur	company
navy	appear	attendance	companion

(3)

neglect	memory	situation	Arithmetic
select	remember	explanation	area
election	intelligent	information	addition
reflection	intention	examination	subtraction

(4)

discuss	equal	divide	religious
discussion	equator	division	marvellous
secret	unusual	decide	delicious
blanket	usually	decision	precious